80p

# Garfield

# On The
# Right Track

## JIM DAVIS

RAVETTE PUBLISHING

First published by
Ravette Publishing Limited 1996
Reprinted 1997

---

Printed and bound in Great Britain
for Ravette Publishing Limited,
Unit 3, Tristar Centre,
Star Road, Partridge Green,
West Sussex RH13 8RA
by Cox & Wyman Ltd, Reading, Berkshire

ISBN 1 85304 907 7

JIM DAVIS 8-5

POKE

I'LL GET YOU FOR THIS

GARFIELD LEFT THE TABLE IN THE MIDDLE OF A MEAL!

© 1994 PAWS, INC./Distributed by Universal Press Syndicate

SNACK TIME

OUT OF DUST RAGS, ARE WE?

JIM DAVIS 8-12

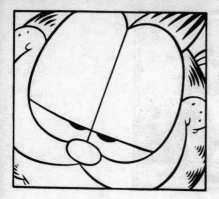

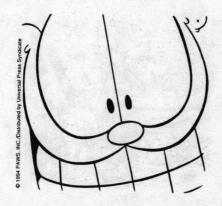

© 1994 PAWS, INC./Distributed by Universal Press Syndicate

© 1994 PAWS, INC./Distributed by Universal Press Syndicate

YEEEOOOOW!

JIM DAVIS 9-13

PLIP

JIM DAVIS 9-15

SWAT!

© 1994 PAWS, INC./Distributed by Universal Press Syndicate

THE THRILL
IS GONE

JIM DAVIS 9-16

© 1994 PAWS, INC./Distributed by Universal Press Syndicate

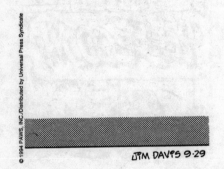

JIM DAVIS 9-29

© 1994 PAWS, INC./Distributed by Universal Press Syndicate

JIM DAVIS 10-4

© 1994 PAWS, INC./Distributed by Universal Press Syndicate

JIM DAVIS 10-10

© 1994 PAWS, INC./Distributed by Universal Press Syndicate

YOU HAVE A LOT
TO LEARN ABOUT
GOOFING OFF

JiM DAViS 10-19

© 1994 PAWS, INC./Distributed by Universal Press Syndicate

© 1994 PAWS, INC. Distributed by Universal Press Syndicate

© 1994 PAWS, INC./Distributed by Universal Press Syndicate

WINTER
IS HERE

DON'T
ANSWER
THE DOOR

JIM DAVIS 12-12

## OTHER GARFIELD BOOKS IN THIS SERIES

| A Garfield Christmas | £3.99 |
| Garfield's Thanksgiving | £2.95 |
| Gallery 3 | £2.99 |
| Gallery 5 | £2.99 |

## GARFIELD THEME BOOKS

| Garfield's Guide to Behaving Badly | £3.99 |
| Garfield's Guide to Insults | £3.99 |
| Garfield's Guide to Pigging Out | £3.99 |
| Garfield's Guide to Romance | £3.99 |